Disney · PIXAR

TOY STORY 4

1001 STICKERS

Autumn Publishing

ALIEN RESCUE

The Aliens are up to mischief. Follow the paths
from Hamm, Slinky Dog and Trixie to discover which
Alien they will rescue before they get into trouble.

A

B

C

1

2

3

Answers on pages 46-47

CLASSROOM CHANGES

It's Bonnie's first day at preschool and she's building a new friend!
Can you spot all eight differences between these two images?

A

B

Answers on pages 46-47

BUDDY BUILDER

Using lots of objects, build your very own
friend in the space below – just like Bonnie did!
Then, give your new friend a name.

REAL FORKY

Only one of these images of Forky is really him. Can you work out which one by following the clues? Circle your answer.

1. Forky is smiling
2. Forky has red arms
3. Forky has a rainbow sticker on his foot
4. Forky's eyes are not the same size
5. Forky is made using a spork

A

B

C

D

E

F

Answers on pages 46-47

WOODY IN PIECES

This picture of Woody and Bo saying goodbye has been ripped up. Can you put the pieces back together? Write your answers in the frame below. The first one has been done for you.

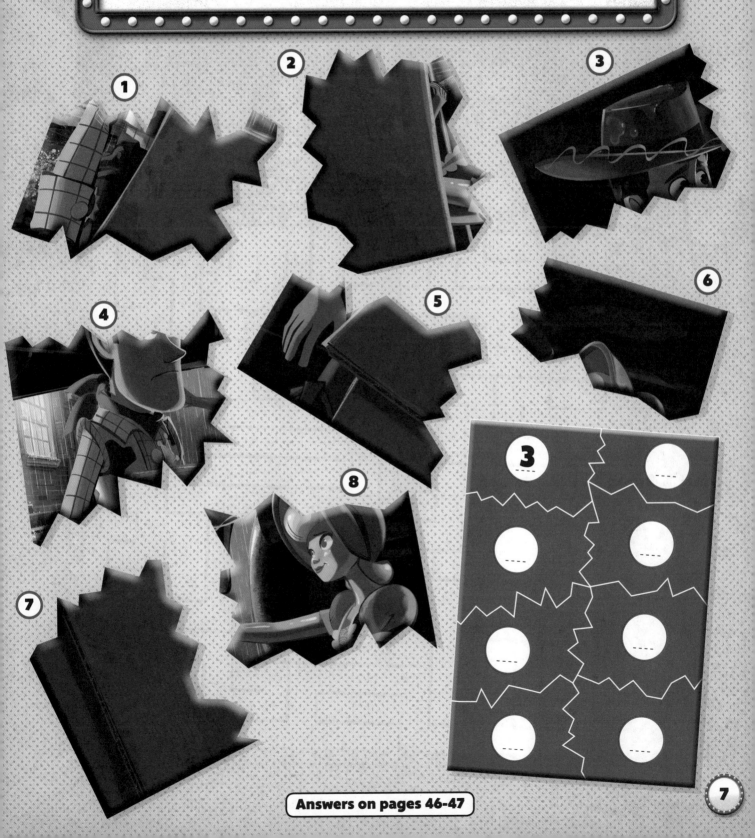

TOY TRAIL

Guide Woody and Bo through the carnival to reach
Second Chance Antiques without being spotted.

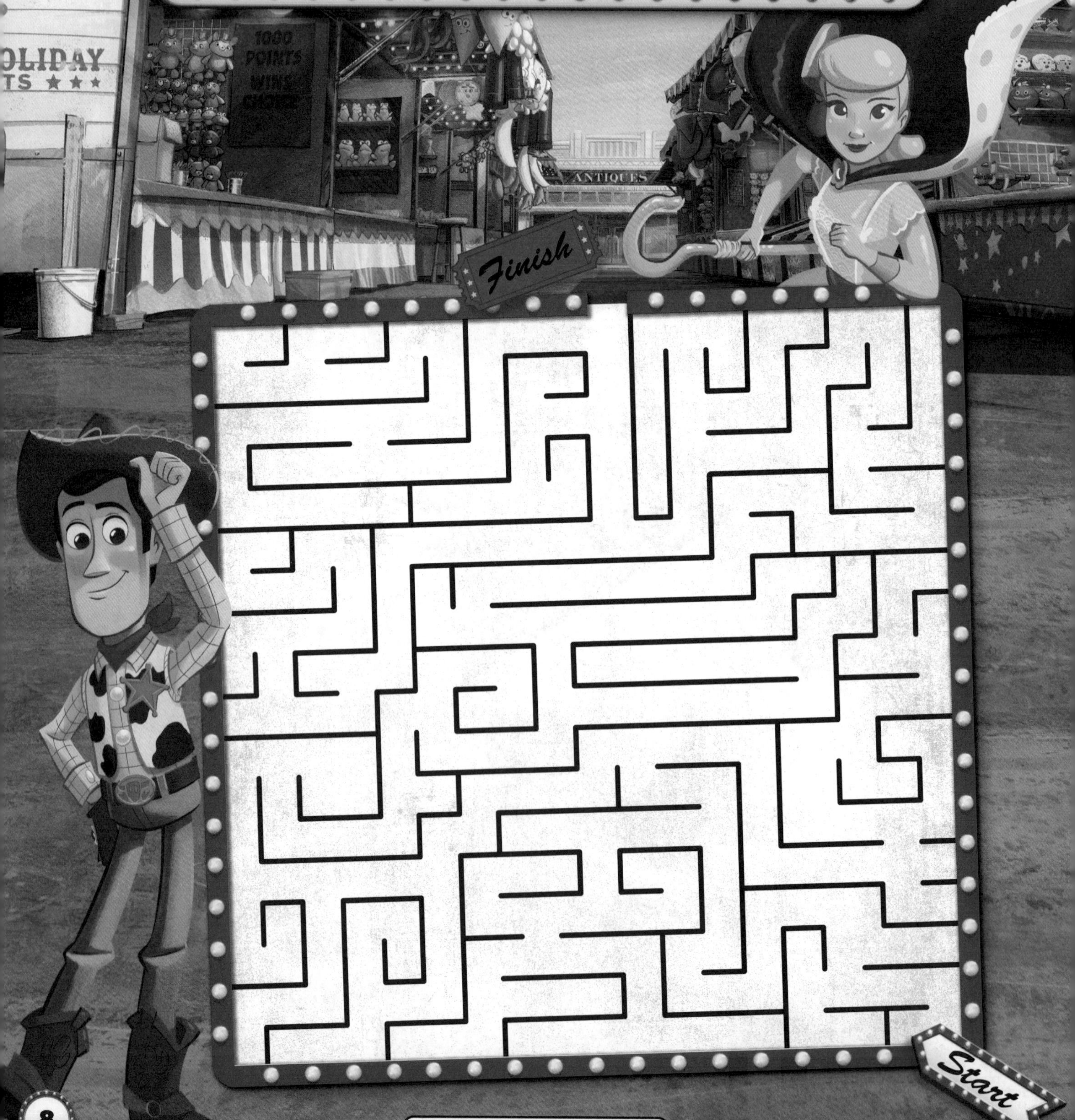

Finish

Start

Answers on pages 46-47

PERFECT PICTURE

Match the close-ups to the correct spaces to complete the picture of Gabby Gabby.

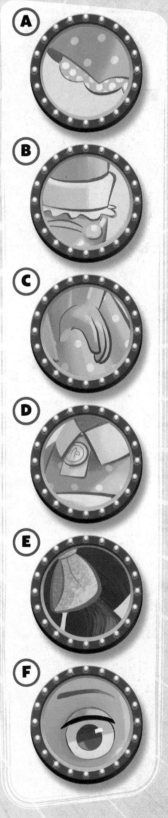

BROKEN

SET THE SCENE

Using stickers from your sticker sheet, fill the
antique shop with all your favourite characters.

JIGSAW JUMBLE

Complete the picture below by working out where the jigsaw pieces belong. Write your answers in the spaces.

Answers on pages 46-47

BO MATCH

Only one of the smaller images of Bo exactly matches the bigger picture. Can you spot which one?

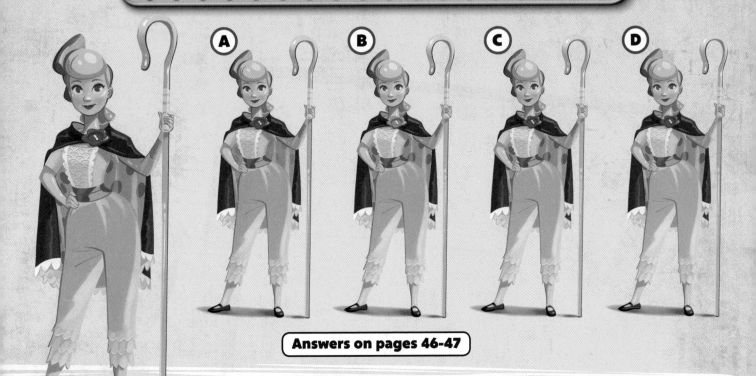

A **B** **C** **D**

Answers on pages 46-47

TIC-TAC-TOY

Playing with a friend, decide who will be noughts and who will be crosses. Take it in turns to fill in an empty space on the grid. The winner is the first person to fill three spaces in a row horizontally, vertically or diagonally.

DINOSAUR DOODLE

Using the grid as a guide, draw this picture of Rex by
copying the squares one by one. Then, colour him in.

PLAYTIME PUZZLE

Complete the puzzle below by making sure each row, box and column contains only one of each character. Write your answers in the spaces.

TOP PRIZE

Ducky and Bunny are taking on Buzz to keep their position as the top prize! With a friend, pick who will play as Ducky and Bunny, and who will play as Buzz. Work out the missing number in each box by adding together the numbers in the two boxes directly below it. The first to reach the top and complete the puzzle is the winner.

```
            [   ]
         [   ][   ]
      [   ][   ][   ]
   [ 2 ][   ][   ][   ]
[ 1 ][   ][ 2 ][ 2 ][ 1 ]
```

Ducky and Bunny

Answers on pages 46-47

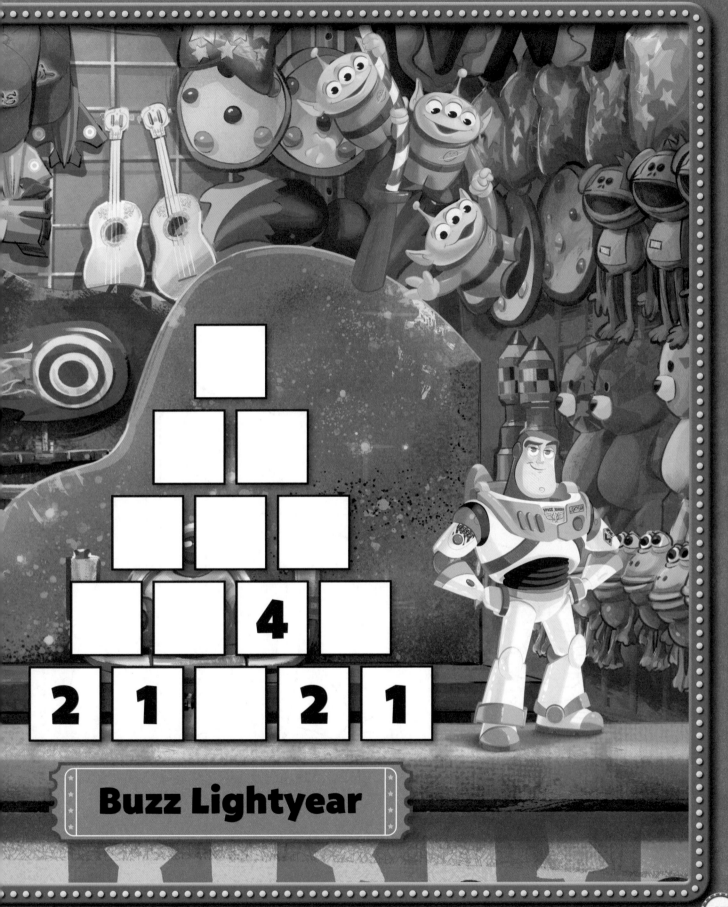

Buzz Lightyear

SEQUENCE SEARCH

Look closely at the grid below and see if you can spot all the sequences shown. Hamm has done the first one for you.

Example ✓

MOSAIC MASTERPIECE

Use the mosaic stickers from your sticker sheets to finish this picture of Ducky and Bunny.

SWEET ROUTE

Following the key below, find the correct route through the candyfloss maze to reach the shop.

Start

Answers on pages 46-47

NAILED IT!

Jessie needs to stop Bonnie and her family leaving – and she has an idea. Guide Jessie through the maze to pop the campervan's tyre. Then, find a path out again!

Start

Finish

Answers on pages 46-47

DOLLY DIFFERENCES

One image of Dolly is different to the others.
Look closely and see if you can spot which one.

A **B** **C**

Answers on pages 46-47

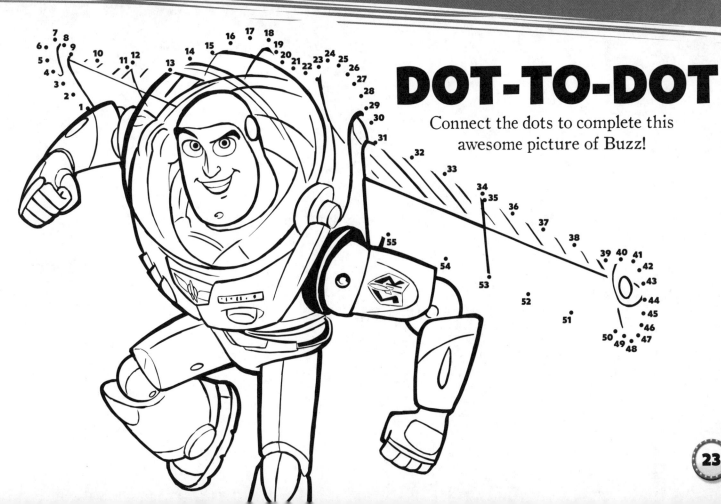

DOT-TO-DOT

Connect the dots to complete this
awesome picture of Buzz!

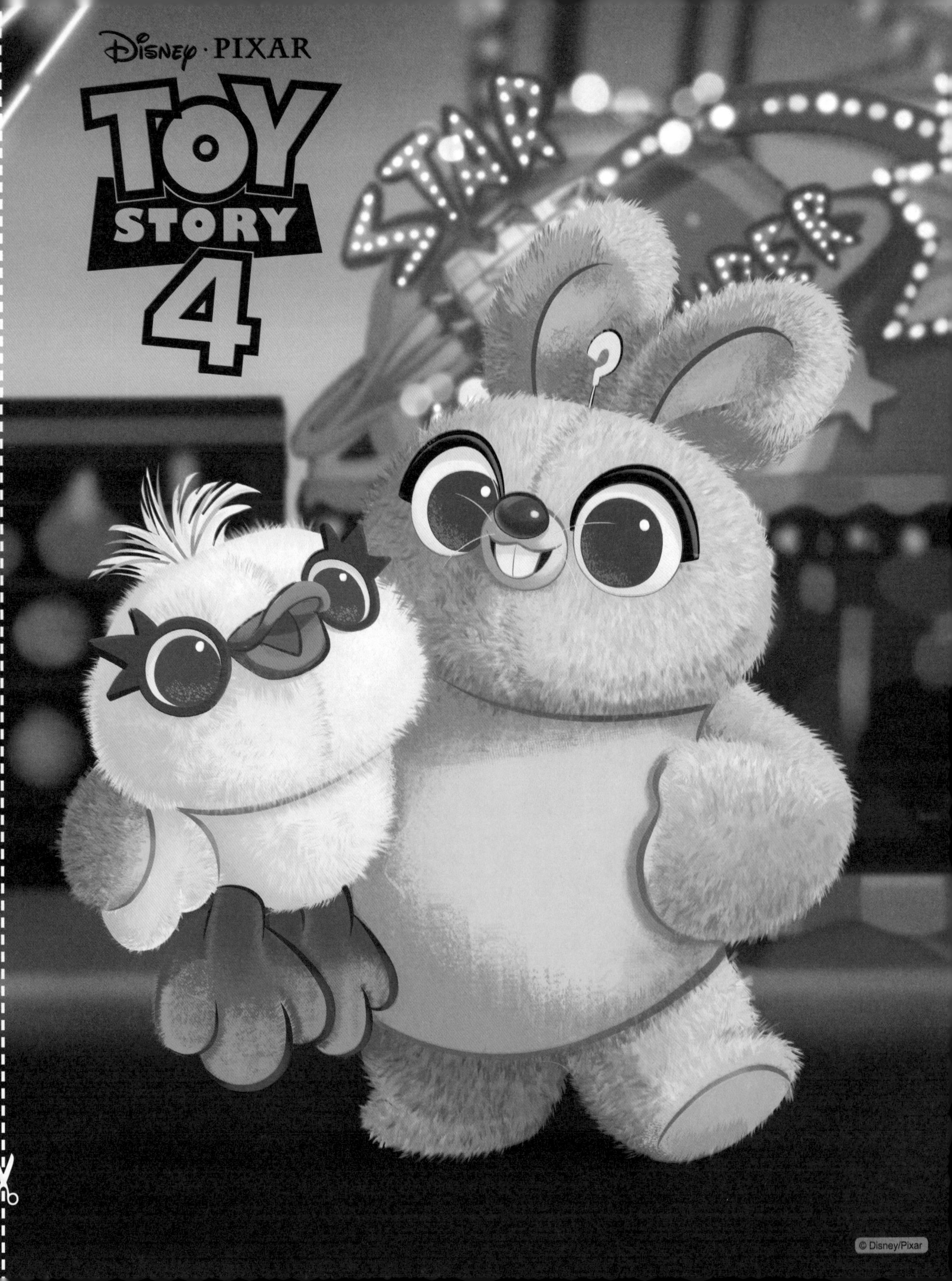
DISNEY · PIXAR
TOY STORY 4

ANTIQUE MIX-UP

This scene in Second Chance Antiques is all jumbled up! Label the images from 1 to 8 to put the pieces back in the right order.

A .....
B .....
C .....
D .....
E .....
F .....
G .....
H .....

Answers on pages 46-47

SQUARE UP

Playing against a friend, the aim is to 'own' as many squares as possible.
Take it in turns to draw a line between two dots horizontally or vertically.
If you complete a box, write your initial inside it. Each box is worth one
point, however if you complete a box with a character in it, award yourself
two points. The winner is the player with the most points at the end.
Write the winner's name in the box at the bottom of the page.

WINNER

COUNTING COLOURS

Look carefully at the jumble of Bo silhouettes. How many of each colour can you count? Write your answers in the boxes below.

....

Answers on pages 46-47

DRAW DUKE

Using the grid as a guide, draw an awesome picture of Duke Caboom!

WILD, WILD WEST

In the space below, draw an amazing wild west scene for Jessie and Bullseye to ride through. Yee-haw!

SHEEP RESCUE

Bo is on a mission to rescue her sheep. Help her reach
Billy, Goat and Gruff by leading her through the maze, but
watch out for the broken paths – you can't cross those!

Finish

Start

PLAYGROUND PALS

The toys are hanging out at the playground.
Can you spot all the toys listed below playing somewhere
in the scene? Tick off each toy when you find them.

Answers on pages 46-47

 1

 2

 3

 4

 5

 6

CUTE CLOSE-UPS

Which close-up below isn't part of this picture of Bo and Giggle McDimples?

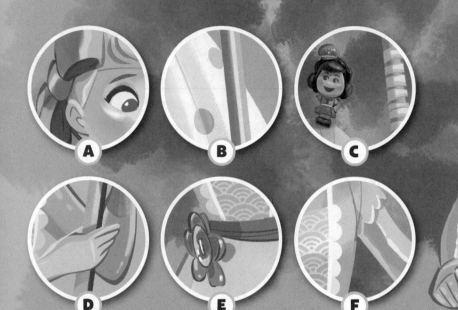

A   B   C

D   E   F

ODD SPORK OUT

One of these images of Forky is slightly different to the others. Can you spot which one?

A   B   C

Answers on pages 46-47

HIGH FLYER

Help Duke Caboom take off by placing your pen on the maple leaf in the centre and following the spiral path as fast as you can without touching the sides.

WHERE'S WOODY?

Woody is hiding out somewhere in the carnival. Follow the puzzles below to work out the coordinates.

Y axis

- Think of a number
- Double it
- Add 9 to it
- Subtract 3 from the total
- Divide the total by 2
- Subtract your original number from the total

X axis

- Think of a number
- Multiply it by 3
- Add 6 to it
- Divide the total by 3
- Subtract your original number

Answers on pages 46-47

BACK TO BONNIE

Lead Forky back to Bonnie by finding the path
that contains sporks that are all the same colour.

SHERIFF SAYS

Using the alphabet key of sheriff badges,
work out what Woody's message says.

Answers on pages 46-47

DOT-TO-DOT

Connect the dots to complete this
picture of Giggle. Then, colour her in!

LIGHTYEAR CLOSE-UPS

Each one of these close-ups belongs somewhere in the bigger picture of Buzz. Can you match them to the correct spaces? Write your answers in the circles.

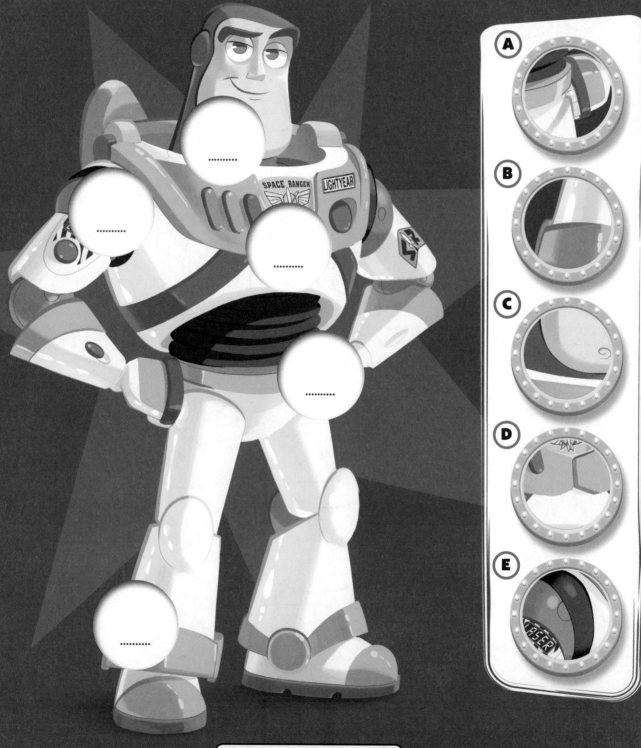

A

B

C

D

E

Answers on pages 46-47

BADGE PATTERNS

Complete these patterns by working out which colour sheriff badges are missing in each line. Use stickers from your sticker sheets to show your answers.

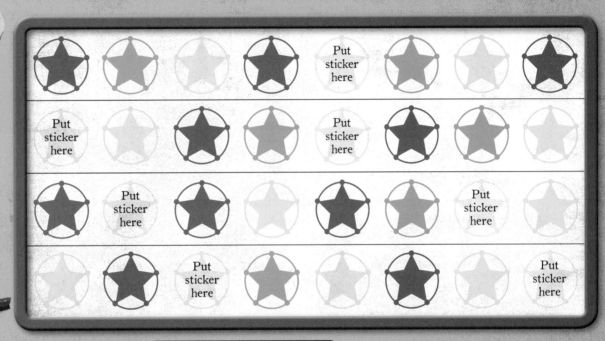

Put sticker here

Put sticker here

Put sticker here

Put sticker here

Put sticker here

Put sticker here

Put sticker here

Put sticker here

Answers on pages 46-47

SCENE IT!

Use stickers from your sticker sheets to build a fun scene on Bonnie's porch.

SPOT THE DIFFERENCES

Billy, Goat and Gruff are very happy to see Woody! There are eight differences between these two images. Can you find them all?

Answers on pages 46-47

ANSWERS

PAGE 2 - ALIEN RESCUE
A-1, B-3, C-2

PAGE 3 - CLASSROOM CHANGES

PAGE 5 - REAL FORKY
E is the real Forky

PAGE 7 - WOODY IN PIECES

PAGE 8 - TOY TRAIL

PAGE 9 - PERFECT PICTURE

PAGE 12 - JIGSAW JUMBLE

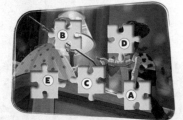

PAGE 13 - BO MATCH
C matches exactly

PAGE 15 - PLAYTIME PUZZLE

PAGES 16 & 17 - TOP PRIZE

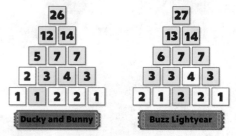

Ducky and Bunny   Buzz Lightyear

PAGE 19 - SEQUENCE SEARCH

PAGE 21 - SWEET ROUTE

ANSWERS

PAGE 22 - NAILED IT

PAGE 23 - DOLLY DIFFERENCES
B is different to the others

PAGE 26 - ANTIQUE MIX-UP
D-1, A-2, H-3, C-4, F-5, E-6, B-7, G-8

PAGE 28 - COUNTING COLOURS

3   5   7   6   8   4

PAGE 31 - SHEEP RESCUE

PAGES 32 & 33 - PLAYGROUND PALS

PAGE 34 - CUTE CLOSE-UPS
D is not part of the picture

PAGE 34 - ODD SPORK OUT
A is different to the others

PAGE 36 - WHERE'S WOODY?

PAGE 37 - BACK TO BONNIE
Path D will lead Forky back to Bonnie

PAGE 38 - SHERIFF SAYS
Nothing keeps a good cowboy down!

PAGE 40 - LIGHTYEAR CLOSE-UPS

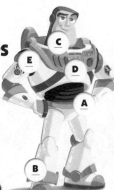

PAGE 41 - BADGE PATTERNS

PAGE 42 - SPOT THE DIFFERENCES